Joy to the World

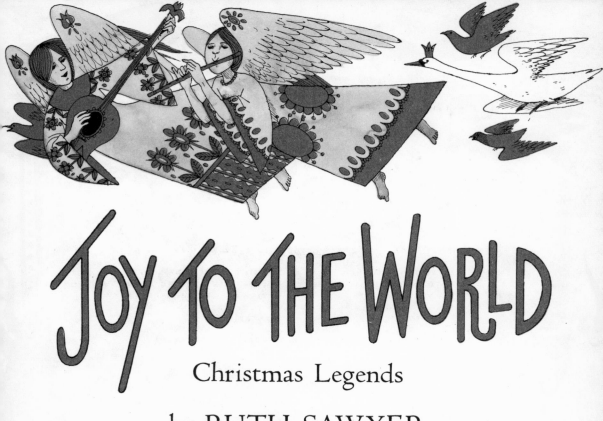

Joy to the World

Christmas Legends

by RUTH SAWYER

Illustrated by Trina Schart Hyman

Little, Brown and Company
Boston   Toronto

Published simultaneously in Canada
by Little, Brown & Company (Canada) Limited

PRINTED IN THE UNITED STATES OF AMERICA

To Ruth Hill Viguers

Down the years we have shared so much in Christmas, in stories told and written. Especially have we shared the eternal substance of Christmas — keeping it as a holy day as well as a holiday.

This last book of Christmas belongs to you as much as it does to me. It goes to you as a small token of our friendship down the years — in New York, in Spain and in Boston, and with my ever-growing admiration for all you have done and all that you are.

So — may Joy to the World *come to you this Christmas season of 1966 with many joyful memories and much love.*

Ruth Sawyer Durand

Joy to the world, the Lord is come!
Let earth receive her King.
Let every heart prepare Him room,
And heaven and nature sing.

Words by Isaac Watts
Music by George Frederick Handel

What This Christmas Book Contains

Joy to the World

A BEDTIME CAROL

At bedtime when I cannot sleep I count my sheep —
   my special sheep.
The first I count is the one that lay
   close to the Christ Child on the hay
   and kept him warm that Christmas Day.

The next was the small lamb who ran free
   in the carpenter's shed near Galilee.
He watched old Joseph as he stood
   making so many things out of wood
   and teaching the little lad all he could.
When work was done and the sun turned red
   lad and lamb left the carpenter's shed
   to eat their supper and share their bed.

The third was a black sheep, a mischievous sheep,
   he ran from his fold and the good shepherd's keep.
He played by the Jordan and he trampled the corn;
   his fleece got tangled in the low, prickly thorn.
But the good shepherd came and the lost one was found;
   with gentle hands he raised him from the hard, winter ground,
   with gentle arms he covered him close from the cold
   and brought him back safely to his own sheepfold.

After I have counted these — my three special sheep —
I feel very drowsy and I always fall asleep.

The Two Lambs

A Legend from Ancient Arabia

IT SO HAPPENS that at the time of Christmas — with its commercialism and weariness — one must reach back into the legendary past to find the true significance. Here is something from Arab folklore. Listen and understand.

In the long, long ago on the far hills of Judea there were pastured many flocks of sheep. Among them were two late-born lambs. They followed their ewes for the best grazing; but they huddled close to their shepherds to listen — to satisfy their curiosity about many things. Now among the shepherds there was an ancient one, well versed in prophecy and tribal lore. As the days waxed colder he began to speak of a great expectancy that was spreading among the Arab and the Hebrew tribes. It concerned a child who was to be born of lowly folk, yet born to be a king.

The two small lambs listened: a child born of lowly folk, to become a king. Here was a great wonderment. Shepherds and sheep were lowly. Could it be that, among the shepherds' huts below, where some brought their families, this baby might be born? Was it among the hills of Judea that the great expectancy would come to pass? The ancient one reminded all who listened that with all great prophecies there comes always some sign, some omen of when the happening might come. And where. But much time passed. Nothing happened. The small lambs grew overeager, troubled. One night as they lay close to their ewes they could not sleep. At last the smaller lamb spoke. "Nothing is ever found unless it is searched for. Not even grass. Come, let us go down the hills and look for this child." So the two small lambs began their search. They looked into every hut; they circled every fire where shepherds lay, keeping watch. They found nothing. "Now where do we go?" asked the larger lamb. "We keep on," said the smaller. Thus they came to a road that wound between the hills. It was the road to Bethlehem — but this they did not know.

As they went the small lamb lifted his eyes to the stars for some sign, some beckoning light. The other lamb plodded along, his eyes on the road, looking for hindrances. At long last he said, "I am tired. There is nothing but foolishness to this search. Sheep are called silly creatures, and that is what we are. I will lay me by the road and sleep until morning; then I will return to my flock." "Lay yourself down and sleep," said the smaller lamb. "I go on."

So the two lambs went their separate ways. Gladness and wonderment welled up in the heart of the smaller lamb as he followed the road. I think his eyes were the first to catch the brightening of the skies and see the star; his ears the first to hear the angels' singing. "I will follow the star — that is the sign," said the lamb. It led him to the lowly stable, the door open to the night. From inside shone radiance; and he could hear the lowing of cattle, the stamping of donkeys' feet. He entered — and inside found the baby, his mother crooning over him. The lamb knelt and nuzzled the tiny hands. He said softly to the shining child: "You will remember and I will remember that a small lamb was the first to find you." Then he departed into the night, to tell all who would listen and understand.

A FRAGMENT FROM A ROMANY CAROL

Now light a candle for God's son
   and one for man, his brother.
Welcome all wanderers this night
   with food and warmth and cover.

A candle light in Mary's name
   and one for Joseph old.
And blessed be all newborn ones
   safe-gathered in God's fold.

This Is the Christmas

A Legend from Serbia

(Serbia is a land of heroes — of strong and great men, of fine and sweet singers. It is a land of much storytelling. The men tell their tales poetry-wise, with words sung rhythmically; the women tell theirs as you or I would tell them. Here is a Christmas story told by Serbian grandmothers for I don't know how many generations.)

IT WAS MIDSUMMER when the great storm came. It swept down through the cut in the mountains into the peaceful valley, ripping the roofs off, laying flat the fields of grain, swelling the river to overflowing. The men worked throughout the night to save their herds, their sheep and goats, driving them to high land. When the sickly, yellow dawn broke, no life had been lost, and one had been gained. On a rock jutting high over the river, a young child was found, crying pitifully.

He was a swarthy, dark-skinned child. Whatever clothes he might have worn the storm had stripped from him. He was too young to do more than babble a few words, and these were in the gypsy tongue. His looks, too, spoke of the Cigani — the gypsies.

It was Father Janovic who found him and brought him to his own cottage, where Mother Janovic was dipping the porridge into the bowls for their own children. Her arms reached out for him as mothers' arms will for all helpless ones. She wrapped him warm in a scrap of blanket. She quieted his sobbing and fed him from her own bowl.

"He is of the Cigani. We will not keep him," said Father Janovic.

"He is very little and helpless. And watch his eyes." Mother Janovic passed her hand up and down in front of his face. There was no blinking. She took up a candle that still burned and passed it so close that the wick almost singed the long dark lashes. But the eyes remained wide, staring. "You see?" said Mother Janovic. "He is blind. You found him. It is the will of God that we keep him." And for that one and only time she gathered the blind boy close to her heart and held him there, crooning soft, loving words over him.

The valley-dwellers of Serbia are hard-working, honest folk, deeply rooted to their land. They do not love the Cigani. They point to the caravans passing through and say: "There go tricksters and thieves. There go the accursed of the earth.

Let no man among us give them harborage." But for all their rascally ways the gypsies have some virtues. They can tell amazing fortunes. They have been known to prophesy the great happenings in the world. They are good farriers and pot-menders. And their music is beloved by all peoples.

But in that long-ago time they were accursed; and the Janovics remembered only this as the blind boy grew older. They called him Marko after their greatest hero — partly in mockery and partly because the boy, like the ancient Marko, loved all small creatures and had a strange way with them. He could call the birds from the woods and they would feed out of his hands. A wounded hare or fox would come whimpering to him for aid. He had tenderness and understanding for all living things. Marking this the Janovics set him at an early age to tend their sheep. Summers he slept with them in the pasture; winters he burrowed under the straw in the shed, holing himself in like a wild creature against the cold. He learned quickly and would have called creature and man alike his brother, had man not despised him.

Because he could not see as other human beings did, he heard what they did not. His fingers and his bare feet soon made him familiar with all the countryside, feeling their way through pasture and woods and along the riverbank. Only upon the village road was he a stranger. Six years after the great storm an old shepherd from Dalmatia crossed the pasture and stopped to make himself friendly. He bore a pipe, self-made; discovering the boy's blindness he played tunes on it and gave it into the boy's hands that he might feel out the fashioning of it.

That summer Marko found a young willow and made his own pipe. Before the first frost came, the boy was making music of his own, strange, wild, haunting music. It stirred the hearts of passers-by; it filled the valley-dwellers with wonder. Before another summer had passed, tales, hard to believe, were being bandied about among them. Some told how on a gentle night, with the moon full overhead, they had heard the lad piping to the lambs and had seen them on their hind legs dancing to the music. Others had seen him pipe the wild hares out of the copses and set them to frolicking in time to a tune as free as the wind.

Mother Janovic did not stint him in his food; but it was ladled out of the big pot, and his bowl was given him to take outside the kitchen. Summers he ate in the pastures; winters in the shed. Only in bitter weather was he bidden inside, to share the warmth of the fire. They were not unkind; only he was set apart from other children, from all humankind. The valley-dwellers made him an outcast from their home and village life.

Do you know what this means — to be cast out from all festivals, all merrymaking? To be forbidden entrance to the church? Once he dared to ask why this should be. "You are of the Cigani, cursed by all the world. The Church, God, Christ and His Blessed Mother are not for you." Mother Janovic said it without unkindness. Father Janovic said it sternly. But the children taunted him with it so that he gave up waiting for them to depart for church, all in their best clothes; but he listened secretly to the music coming from its door, wide-opened to all but him.

He became a silent boy, save for the music he made and the words he sometimes sang between the pipings. His elders marked this with approval and quoted an old Slav proverb: "He who preserves silence speaks well." In lambing time Marko watched over the ewes so well that rarely was a lamb lost. Those that came into the world too feeble to fight for themselves the first few hours, he warmed against his own body, under his tunic. For all his blindness he would have been a happy boy had the people of the valley made him a dweller with them. Yet in an odd way, they were proud of him and stood in awe of his powers to make music and to call wild things to him. They listened stealthily to his songs and pipings; and often a stranger coming into the valley would hear a farmer, ploughing behind his oxen, singing:

Plough — plough — break the good soil —
    Seed for the sowing,
    Sun for the growing.

Harvest and thresh the grain, fill the full measure —
    Bread for the making,
    Straw for the baking.

Fathers and mothers and little ones gather —
    Let bread be broken,
    Let thanks be spoken.

" 'Tis a good song, a new one to me. From where comes it?" This a man from the north or south would ask; and the farmer would answer: " 'Tis only a jingle made by one of our shepherds — a blind boy and not one of us."

How often Marko heard this! Yet it tied no strings to his pipe, it hung no bitterness across his heart. But he did know sorrow. Every time he turned toward the valley when the church bell rang; every time he listened to a gathering of dancers in the village square, with old Stefan making music on his fiddle, the sorrow deepened. But it was worse at Christmas time. To have no part in all the gaiety and beauty of the Christ's Holy Eve and Day — that brought a full weight of sorrow.

To lie in the cold and dark of the Holy Eve, just before the midnight service, and to hear Mother Janovic waking the rest of the children: "Come, Vuk. Come, Ivo. Come, Draga; we have haste to make." But never: "Come, Marko." To hear the bustling, the calling of one to another in the cottage; and to know he was the outcast, forbidden to have a part in that

Christ Service; and later to hear the hurrying of feet along the road. That made of sorrow a load almost too much to bear. Once he followed, feeling his way across the barnyard to the road, following the sound of the ringing bell. If he could not enter, he could stand at the door and listen; and coming home he could whisper the part he was forbidden to sing in the carols.

But his feet knew not the valley-road. There were no familiar stones, rises or hollows to guide him. All was confusion, until, having stumbled off and on again many times, fear came. He turned and somehow stumbled back to the shed. There he lay in his straw, shaking with the cold and the fright.

The priest, a kindly man, tried to teach him something of the Church, of God and the birth of Christ, so that he would not live and die in absolute ignorance. He would stop often when the boy was tending sheep and sit with him for an hour or so, letting the boy ask questions. "This God — he is the Big King?"

"You may call him that, lad."

"And the Christ, who was the Baby Jesus in the Manger, he is the Small King, yes?"

"Even so."

"And Mary? She was the Small King's mother — and very holy? Are they all in the church, yonder?"

"They are in Heaven. Their images only are in the church."

"But if I entered I could feel their faces? I could feel each line until I knew them as I know my sheep."

The old priest sighed. "It is the law of the church. We cannot break it. The people of the valley would not permit it. They have consecrated the church with their vows — even as a bishop of long ago consecrated it with holy water. No Cigani may enter."

"And would my entering defile it?"

"So they think. When God bade Joseph, Mary, and the Child flee to Egypt, the Cigani — the Egyptians — denied them shelter, food, and care. It is a long tale. Sometime I will tell you it."

"For this we are cursed?"

"Truly."

"And shall we never have a part in Christmas?"

"Short of some miracle, never, my son, never. It is the mark you must bear, the mark of the outcast."

Marko drew in his breath; slowly he let it out with words: "Take my hand. Put it on that place where my body bears the mark, and I will cut it out."

"It lies not upon your body, my son, but on your soul."

There followed a long silence; at last the boy asked his final question: "Why call you me 'my son'?"

The old priest sighed again: "Truly, I know not. I am but a simple man."

On Christmas Day, early, it was the custom for the other boys to gather wood for the great village fire, where sucking pigs would roast all day, turned on their spits. Some one chosen boy would go from house to house and greet each household: "The Christ is born!" And the mother, scattering a handful of wheat to bring plenty into the house, would answer: "In truth, He is born." Then the boy would beat the Christ Log on the hearth until a great streaming of sparks mounted and he would wish: "May the Holy Christmas bring as many sheep and goats, pigs and cattle and bees as there are sparks mounting the chimney."

Marko wished he might have been that boy just once, to wish plenty on the valley. He wished he might have taken his place, just once, for the feast and had his share of the sucking pigs. But never for him! Had not the priest said it would take a miracle, nothing short of that would lift the curse? Yet, if he could not share the Christmas, worship in church on the Holy Eve, sing the carols, he could make a carol of his own and worship in the shed. That would not be so different from the place the Bethlehem shepherds had come to, to worship the Small King in his manger.

It happened in that year when he was twelve. Father Janovic had marked the years since the great storm in notches with his scythe against an upright of the shed; and Marko, with his fingers, checked his age. He had been two or thereabouts when rescued, and there were ten notches. That Holy Eve, a ewe-lamb became tangled in a thorn-tree, and being frightened she jumped about so frantically that her leg was broken. Marko tore his tunic to strips, and taking wood bound the leg. Kneeling, he lifted her across his shoulders, and holding her fast by her good legs, he bore her to the shed and laid her down in his corner of straw. Then, stretched beside her he talked softly to her, as if she had been kin and human: "This is the night the Christ is born. We will keep the Christmas, thou and I. Thou shalt hear my carol, made through the long days of ripening wheat, birds whirling southward, winds telling of winter. Thou shalt worship with me, here, when stroke of bell rings out from that church we may not enter."

The ewe lay quietly beside the boy, each warming the other. They slept a little, I think, awoke, and slept again. Then, through the cold of approaching midnight came the voice of Mother Janovic calling her children: "Come, Vuk. Come, Ivo. Come, Draga, we must make haste." If only she might call one more name, call it joyously: "Come, Marko!"

But that would never be, short of a miracle. And when had a miracle taken place in the valley here? The blind boy's hand felt for the lamb; his fingers worked in and out of the thick fleece. His other hand held his pipe, close. "Thou knowest it

not, small one, but when a human stands in dire need of help
— when calamity comes and he needs a friend, a protector,
one to be to him as might a brother be, he can ask for such
help and it cannot be denied him. That is a law among the
Serbian people. Dost thou think that if I should pray this
night — in my great need — that holy ears in Heaven would
hear?"

There came from the road the sound of many feet, brisk
and eager feet, young and old. The slow ringing of the bell
began, calling all within the valley to come and worship the
newborn King.

Marko rose to his knees. Again he spoke to the lamb:
"Small one, I have heard it said that on the Christ Eve all
dumb creatures kneel upon the hour the Christ was born.
Canst kneel?"

As if at his bidding the ewe-lamb shook herself, rose upon
her hind legs, even upon the one that had been broken, and
bent her forelegs on the straw. Again the blind boy's hand
moved comfortingly through the thick fleece. He prayed:
"Big King — send one to sponsor me — one who will speak
for me among the valley-folk. For I would be as other boys,
welcome at table, called to church by the bell, having a share
in worship and the Christ Eve."

The bell stopped ringing. Marko felt a stirring not far off,
feet rustling the straw. Then a strange hand was placed upon
his shoulder.

Marko spoke in wonder: "Can words reach Heaven faster than a bird flies?"

"Some words can."

"Did the Big King send you to be my sponsor?"

"Perhaps. Perhaps to bear you company, that you need not be alone this Christ Eve."

"Who are you?"

"A boy, even as yourself."

"Blind?"

"Not blind. But are you blind? Think."

"People call me blind, and I would see. I would see the whole wide world and all it holds."

"No one sees that. But think — in that little piece of world that lies about you, have you not found more beauty than have those who see? Do they know the small loveliness of a bird's feather? Do they hear what the wind whispers? Have they caught the song the morning stars sing? And can they put all these things into music and play it on a pipe as you can?"

"But I would see."

"It is not given for any one person in this life to have too much. Would you bargain your music away for the power to see only what most humans see? Think."

"I am thinking. This I know. I would see once the face of the Small King."

A hush had fallen on the shed, on the valley, on the whole

world. The words Marko heard were barely whispered: "Put your fingers on my face. Trace every line, slowly, so you will remember."

Lightly as winter snow the hand of the blind boy touched the face held close to his own — tracing forehead, feeling the wide-set eyes, the rounded cheek, the slender clear-cut nose, the strong molded chin. He nodded, his own face lighting with exaltation as each feature became familiar, possessed. Then he sighed with deep tranquillity. "I will keep the music. I will be a singer for the people of Serbia."

He put his pipe to his lips and blew the tune for his carol. Between the pipings he sang the words he had made:

This is the Christmas.
>   To Mary most blessed,
>   Jesus, the Saviour, is born.

These are the angels —
>   Singing through Heaven,
>   All curses forgiven this morn.

These are the shepherds.
>   They seek for the Stranger,
>   They kneel at the manger, to pray.

And I — a blind shepherd —
>   Give prayer to the Big King,
>   Give song to the Small King — this day.

The midnight service over, the valley-folk poured out upon the road. A dazzling light filled the sky. It shone over the whole valley. "It comes from there!" said one. "No, from yonder it comes," said another. Hands pointed everywhere. The priest, who had shepherded them to the doorway of the church, pointed to Janovic's farm: "It is from there it comes."

He led the way. When they came to the farmyard, they found the small, mean shed bathed in light. No word was spoken. Massed about the low doorway they stood, unbelieving what their eyes told them. For they could see within, kneeling on the straw, the blind boy; and kneeling with him were a small ewe-lamb and the Christ. A circle of light shone about His head, making such brightness as the valley-folk had never seen upon the earth.

All bent their heads as in church worship. The old priest spoke in low humility: "The miracle. It is we who have been blind. It is upon our heads the curse comes home to rest." And picking up his robe he knelt on the fringe of the straw. The valley-folk knelt with him, making no stir in the night. The blind boy piped on, singing his carol over again and again in his great gladness.

A CAROL FROM AN IRISH CABIN

The cold wind blows over the heather,
    The salt wind blows over the sea,
The harsh wind blows down from the mountains,
    And blows a white Christmas to me.

The clean snow falls softly, falls softly,
    The snow crystals cover the moor.
Let wanderers lost and grown weary
    Find welcome at my cabin door.

So let there be no fear of darkness,
    And let there be no fear of sea;
Let the star guide the lost and forsaken
    Safe over the moorland to me.

The cold wind blows over the heather,
    The salt wind blows over the sea,
The harsh wind blows down from the mountains,
    And brings a white Christmas to me.

The Precious Herbs of Christmas

An Irish Fairytale

HIS NAME was Goodlad. The wise woman of the Lough had named him, bending over his cradle soon after he was born. "He has the look of a good lad," she had said.

And his mother had answered, " 'Tis a good name. I shall pray that he grows up to bear it well!"

Soon after Goodlad was born, his father died. That left just his mother and himself and made him the man of the family. They lived on the side of Binn Ban in a small cabin, its back against a great rock to give shelter against the bitter wind of winter. Its strong chimney and thatched roof kept off the rain. Inside, the single room was snug and pleasant. There was an outshot bed with a trundle under for Goodlad. There was a dresser with gay dishes, a deep hearth that drew well, with a crane to hold the black pot that cooked the stir-about, the potatoes, and the cabbages. And there was a griddle for bread. Little of meat they ever tasted, but Goodlad grew strong and sturdy.

He learned to tend a flock of goats, cutting a pipe from a
sallywand that he might call them to him. He fetched water
from the Lough and cut rushes with which to strew the clay-
packed floor of the cabin. He cut turf from the bog to keep
their fire; and when he was seven, he had strength in his
fingers to milk the goats. There was milk enough for Goodlad
to drink, for his mother to put in her strong, firm tea, and
enough to make cheese. Some they ate and much they sold.

He lingered often at the Lough when work brought him
there, listening to the skylark soar upwards, singing its
matins, listening to the throstle's bubbling song — all things
that had music or beauty he held close to his heart. Of one
thing only he had fear — the night. When darkness fell he
would beg his mother to heap more turf on the fire, to draw
the curtains hard against the night, and to light the candle.
Then would he draw his creepie close to her chair and ask
for tales of the good people, the fairies. There were those
who put no stock in aught that was good in the fairies. They
would say to him, "Goodlad, ye are foolish entirely to believe
in their goodness. They bring only mischief to humanfolk."

But the lad thought otherwise; and no one could shake his
faith in them. He would save some of his stirabout at night
and put it out with a small piggin of milk; and when he found
it gone in the morning, he would say with glee, " 'Tis the
good people themselves I have fed this night."

His mother knew a host of tales to tell: of the fairies who had filled the meal chests in famine years — the same ones who had made many pairs of brogues when old Tomas, the cobbler, fell ill — and of the fairy pot of gold hidden under a blackthorn and who had found it. And always there was the tale of a White Christmas, when the fairies came out of their raths and brought some lucky gift for a lad or a lass they liked. The tales of a White Christmas Goodlad liked best.

Often, when the tale finished, his mother would take the lad with her to the door, throw it wide, and say, "Look ye! Can ye see aught in the night to bring fear to a lad? What does darkness hold that day has not? Stars, just. And each bes a candle lighted by God's own hand. Cannot ye hear His whispering on the night wind? The night holds naught of fear. Go to bed, Goodlad, with a brave heart." But nothing his mother said lifted the fear from him.

He had passed eight and was feeling himself to be a man, when he had his adventure with one of the good people. It was dusk and three times Goodlad had blown his pipe to call the goats back for their milking, and none had come. With an eye to the daylight left and with heavy feet he climbed the slope of Binn Ban, looking for the flock. He had gone not far when he heard a faint whimpering sound come from beyond the next turn of the goatspath. Could the youngest born have fallen and hurt its leg? He stumbled on in the gathering gloom to find not a small goat but a wee fairyman who had fallen in a crevice of a rock and was unable to get himself out.

The lad peered downward. He could see the little man pinned fast with his legs bent under him. His small hands were torn with their catching at the ragged rock, his red cap was awry, and he looked pitiful entirely. Kneeling, Goodlad called to him, "Have a brave heart, wee man. I'll have ye safely out in the whisk of a goat's tail." And that he did.

Settling him carefully upon his feet, Goodlad brushed him off and set his cap straight. The wee man's face was wrinkled all over like the bark of a cedar; and it took long for the breath to come back to him. When it did, he asked, "Speak out, lad. What is it you bes wanting?"

"Wanting? I am at a loss to know what ye mean."

"A wish, lad, a wish. Are ye not knowing that when humanfolk give help to fairyfolk they can ask for whatever they wish and it must be granted?"

"But I have no wish," said the lad.

"Think hard. Is there not a single thing you would be having?"

Goodlad shook his head. "There is naught."

The fairyman looked at him with great puzzlement. " 'Tis a great pity. Likely ye'll live to regret it." He shook his head with wonder and repeated, " 'Tis a great pity. I might then leave behind me the promise of a wish, but I am the last one to promise it might come true." And with that he was gone,

whither Goodlad could never have told; but down the goats-path came Star, the lead goat, with the flock following her.

That night it was Goodlad who had a tale to tell after the candle was lighted and the curtains drawn. This happened in midsummer; and when the first sharp wind of winter blew over Binn Ban, the lad's mother was taken with a strange illness.

Goodlad brewed one after another of the herbs he had gathered with her, holding the cup to her lips and watching eagerly for some small sign of betterment; but none came. He tended and milked the goats, drew water, cut turf, kept the cabin tidy, and tried to tease the sick woman's appetite with all the food he could find. A time came when she turned her head away from him. Her laughter was gone; she lay all day, silent, with barely the sign in her eyes of knowing him, her lad.

The time came at long last when she seemed to be sleeping. With hope nearly gone from him Goodlad took the path that led to the wise woman of the Lough. He found her huddled close to her hearth. She nodded as he drew a creepie close to her. "Is the mother no better?" she asked.

"She is failing, fast. Each day she is slipping further from me. I must know. What can heal her?"

Silence fell between them. When she answered, the wise woman was shaking her head as if she had little hope. Slowly she spoke the words that were to fill Goodlad with fear.

"There is but one thing that can heal her, the precious herbs of Christmas. There must be seven of them, gathered in the dark-of-the-moon, with the falling of the first snow upon them. This means a White Christmas. A twig of each herb must be brewed and taken before the crowing of the first cock on Christmas Day."

"But where shall I find the precious herbs? I know only the common ones."

"Ye must search for them. Ye must gather them gently, seeing that each stalk holds the snow that has fallen on it, for they must be brewed with the fresh-fallen snow."

"The dark-of-the-moon! That means night. I can never do it. I will be too afeared."

"Does that matter — if it means bringing your mother to good health again?"

"But I have never gone into the night. I will be too afeared."

"Love casteth out all fear."

Those were the words he carried away with him. But how was a wee lad like himself to brave the dark? How find precious herbs when he knew none of them? What if it were not a White Christmas! With the words mingled all these doubts. It was a sad, a troubled lad who reached his cabin at last to find the goats waiting to be milked and the fire needing turf.

Through the days that followed, fear and doubt grew. His mother worsened. The clouds that gathered gave no snow.

So came the Holy Eve. All the day the sky was clear; not until dusk drew in did the sky darken and the wind blow chill. All through a long-waiting day he had prayed — first that the Christmas would be white and that by some miracle his courage would come back to him; then that there might be no snow, and snug and safe he might stay inside the cabin no matter what befell his mother. The last words of the wise woman of the Lough came back to him all through the gathering dusk: "Love casteth out fear — love casteth out fear."

Goodlad came at last and stood beside his mother's bed. She opened her eyes and met his, still full of fear and doubt. But he spoke bravely, "I must be gone a while. Promise me ye will be here when I come back. Promise me ye will bide till Christmas Day."

The promise was made; and it was then Goodlad knew he was bound by that promise. A happy thought came to him: he would take the goats for company. It could be that Star, leading the way, might bring him to that spot where grew the precious herbs.

There was not a star in the sky; yet still no snow fell. He loosed the goats from the byre and let Star choose the path. The sound of the goat's bell with its low tinkle through the darkness ahead gave a lift to his courage. The remembering that he had put the lighted candle in the window of the cabin added to his courage. In spite of the darkness that enfolded him, his feet followed the goats, nimble as they were, and soon he knew he had climbed higher than he had ever gone on Binn Ban.

Suddenly he was conscious of two things. Something cold had brushed his cheek — a snowflake; and ahead Star had stopped, the goats crowded close around. As Goodlad stopped he could make out the goats, kneeling together on a high sharp ridge. He huddled close to them for comfort. He could see the star on the lead goat's forehead shine out in the darkness with a misty light. The snow began with heaviness and was fast covering the ground. It would be a White Christmas. Goodlad could feel his heart lift within him.

As he peered downward into the meadowland some distance below the sharp ridge on which he and the goats were lying, he caught the glimmer of tiny twinkling lights coming towards him. At first they appeared to be clusters of stars, bobbing along the snow-covered meadow; but as they came closer, he could make out that each was borne by a small, wee figure, a fairyman — one of the good people. There must have been hundreds and hundreds of them, and the hundreds and hundreds of tiny lights brought a shining splendor to the white snow. A merry sight it was, and the lad's heart leaped with delight. "The good people, the good people," he said over to himself and the goats. The fairies circled beneath him, the foremost one seeming so close that Goodlad felt he could almost have touched the peak of the leader's red cap.

They made not a sound in their coming. Heavier and heavier the snow fell. Suddenly the silence was shattered by a small shrill voice. " 'Tis a White Christmas. Ye are all well knowing what has fetched us abroad this night."

Another shrill voice answered, "The granting of a wish to some mortal this night."

"Aye. But to which mortal shall it be granted?"

Again silence fell on the meadow, the ridge, and those gathered there. Then the first voice spoke again, "Ye are all remembering that at last midsummer I fell into a deep crevice on Binn Ban and could not lift myself out. A small lad with gentle fingers saved me, brushed me tidily, and would ask no wish. 'Tis the same lad that has shared his stirabout and milk with us many a time. Tonight there lies an unspoken wish on his lips, and heavy it lies on his heart. Ye know full well what the wish is. Shall it be granted or no?"

The silence this time lay on them all — as deep as the gathering snow. And the voice that broke it whispered soft as a falling flake, "Let the wish be granted. 'Tis a good wish, wished by a brave heart. But haste must be made. Seven of the precious herbs of Christmas must be marked by rush-lights. Care must be taken that the snow is left hanging on each one. There are but a few moments left before the first cock will crow."

The hundreds of tiny figures formed a ring. In and out

they wove, with here, with there a fairyman breaking the ring to step aside and hang his rush-light on a low clump of what seemed to the watching lad to be weeds. They hummed a merry tune as they circled. Soon words were set to rhythm:

Softly, softly, softly — let us make no sound,
As we weave a fairy ring on our fairy ground.
Hang each fairy light with care where the good herbs grow;
Let no fairy hand shake off the white, fresh-fallen snow.

Sing the song of gentle folk, magic spread afar;
Let it touch a human lad following his star.
Let it lift from his wee heart all the fear of the dark,
Seven lights on seven herbs. Lad — look well and mark!

Wonder filled the small lad nestled close to his goats as he watched the seven rush-lights hung on seven low branches. And even as he watched, the hundreds of fairymen with the lights they still carried were gathered up in a thick cloud with the strong whispering of wind in the air.

When the cloud vanished over the rim of the meadow, the snow had stopped; and in the rifts of the breaking cloud stars sprang low in the sky. Into Goodlad's thoughts came as suddenly the memory of his mother's words: "Stars, just. And each bes a candle lighted by God's own hand." And with the words, he saw Star rising to her feet, the other goats following; gently down the slope they went, Goodlad after them.

The hands that broke a branch from each marked herb were steady. Not a flake of snow was lost. Star led the way back to the cabin on nimble feet. The lad was home, the candle still burning in the window, the goats going of their own will to the byre. Then Goodlad was within — fresh turf on the fire, a sprig from each of the seven herbs broken into the small pot, the snow still covering them before the heat of the cabin melted it. The herbs were brewed in a trice — strong, giving forth good fragrance. Carefully he poured the liquid into a cup and, carrying it to where his mother lay, he called to her eagerly, " 'Tis the precious herbs of Christmas. Smell the good healing in them. Open your eyes, mother of mine, and drink quickly before the first cock crows." He held the cup to her lips as he raised her head, which had been sunk deep in the pillow. Slowly the lids lifted, slowly the lips tasted, and she drank. The cup was empty, drained just as the first cock lifted its call to the rising sun.

Long Goodlad stood over his mother after he had let her head slip back. For the first time in many days her lips parted in a gentle smile; then her eyes closed and she was asleep. Many times the lad came back to her, marking the breathing, marking the faint tinge of color coming back to her cheeks. "The promise has been granted, the precious herbs found, and again she will be well and her laughter fill the cabin." His face shone in wonderment.

Suddenly he knew he must look with care at each precious herb that he might know them again, should his mother fall ill. He had left the herbs on the dresser, and now he took them to the window through which the growing light of a Christmas Day was streaming. One by one he scanned them, naming each as he passed it from one hand to the other: "Camomile — tansy — pennyroyal — rue — heal-all — thyme — yarrow. They bes common herbs, all of them." The same he had helped his mother to gather from the time he could first walk. What was the meaning of this!

It was too much for him to understand. When his mother was well again, she would explain — or the wise woman of the Lough. It was enough now that he knew these common herbs had become, by some wondrous misadventure, the precious herbs of Christmas.

When dark fell, there came to Goodlad another wondrous thing. This night he felt no need to draw the curtains, to build up the fire, or to light the candle against the coming of darkness. He went to the door and flung it wide and spoke his thankfulness to the coming stars:

> The night is not a fearsome thing,
> The night is not a fearsome thing,
> The night is not a fearsome thing!

And across the cabin, listening, his mother heard the words and added her thankfulness to his. What a time to remember — this White Christmas.

A CHILD'S CAROL FOR EPIPHANY

Oh, Three Kings, will you ride tonight — oh will you ride
again,
As you rode so very long ago to far-off Bethlehem?

And will you bring those splendid gifts you brought in days
of old —
The gifts you brought the Little King, frankincense, myrrh
and gold?

And every child will wait this night, hoping that you will
bring
A honey cake, a little toy — oh, Kings — most anything.

Enough — so not one child forgets that Three Kings ride
again
To a stable and a manger and a child in Bethlehem.

What the Three Kings Brought

A Personal Christmas Story

THIS IS A PERSONAL Christmas story. I spent a year in Spain some time ago. During the holiday season, by strange chance, I had a sharing in one of the oldest and loveliest of the Christmas legends. On Twelfth Night, or Epiphany, the Three Kings still ride from the East. To the children of the rich they bring *regalos,* or gifts; to the children of the poor they bring a *regalito,* a little gift.

I had spent *Nochebuena* — the Good Night — and Christmas Day in Spanish Morocco and I reached Seville five days before the Three Kings would ride. It was bitterly cold that winter; there were few tourists. The large hotels were nearly empty; the small family hotel where I stayed had only a scattering of guests. Everywhere one felt the suffering and poverty of the people. Yet I had been long enough in Spain to know that with a festival only five days off, everyone, in spite of the hunger and cold, would be ready to celebrate joyfully, even with little food and a little gift.

The first morning I walked out to the Parque Maria Luisa to see the *glorietas*. These are tributes to the most famous of the Spanish writers, little intimate patios with tile benches and bookcases. In the *glorieta* to Cervantes, where atop each bookcase rode delightful figurines of Don Quixote and his faithful Sancho Panza, I caught up with the park attendant bringing back the books to fill the bookcases. He was small and old and friendly. I found that his name was Alfredo and that he had packets of seed to sell that one might feed the birds. The birds were also friendly.

Before the morning was half over and all the books were back in the *glorietas,* Alfredo joined me and whistled the birds out of their trees, some to pick up seeds at our feet, some to take them out of our hands.

The next morning being sunny and warmer, I walked out again to the park and found Alfredo had a helper. He brought him up and introduced him with that courtesy I always found among the simple folk of Spain. "This is Pepe, *señora*. He has come a long way from a farm in the uplands. He hopes to earn enough money to buy a burro for his *papá*. So now you will please buy your seeds from Pepe."

He stood there close to Alfredo, a scrawny ill-fed little boy with eyes far too large for his face. He wore the thin black cotton knickers of the poor and a ragged jacket out at the elbows but neatly patched. His legs were bare; his feet, thrust into the *alpargatas,* the canvas, rope-soled shoes of the common folk, were blue with cold. As I looked at him, I wondered if he knew how many hundreds of seed-packets he must sell to buy a burro.

The three of us stood in silence for a little moment, and then pride and a deep love loosened Pepe's tongue: "I would have you know, *señora,* that the *papacito* is a good farmer. But he has been sick and there are many mouths to feed. When the autobus ran over our burro, the *papacito* had heavy loads to carry. This he must not do so I have come to buy a young, strong burro to help make him well again — the *papacito.*"

I looked down, more concerned now for the thin body, the pinched face and the courage that brooked no defeat. "I will take ten packets of seeds every morning, and perhaps you will tell me more about your family and the *papacito* who takes such good care of you all."

A smile broke through as money and packets changed hands. Courage spoke again in his last words: "I am right to help him — yes? You see I am the oldest and almost a man."

"You are indeed, *hombre.* I can see you already riding that burro the long distance home. *Buen' suerte.*" So did I wish him good luck and went back to the hotel.

That night, a young Jewish scholar, also staying at my hotel, asked if he might join me for dinner. He had come on a fellowship to do research work in history at the Archives in Seville. His grant barely covered his expenses and he was homesick after three months of hard work and little companionship. So I told him about Pepe and my morning in the park. I have always found the Jewish people quick and warm with their sympathy. Abraham was eager to know more; his questions came fast: "How old is this Pepe? Where is he living in the city? How much does a good burro cost? Why has Alfredo given the boy so much hope when he must know only too well he could never earn enough even to buy a goat?"

I could answer only one of the questions, but I defended Alfredo. The man had honesty and kindness. He had his reasons for encouraging the boy. As for the cost of burros, it had so happened that I had gone that afternoon to the market to price them. I had priced all kinds of burros — young, old, starved and well-fed, and each burro had his own price. "In American money, a good burro would cost all of twenty dollars, probably more."

Abraham shook a sad head: "After paying for board and room and the many photostats I must have, there isn't enough left to pay for the hoof of one burro. How about you?"

I shook my head. "If I had enough it would never be the way to do it. Pepe has a great pride, first for himself — almost a man — then for the *papacito*. To hand out the money and say 'Go, buy that burro,' would hurt him terribly. We must find some other way."

We finished our dinner and sat in a long silence, thinking. Abraham spoke first. "Look. Suppose I play hookey from the Archives tomorrow and we go to the park together. How can I think of a plan to buy that burro until I see the boy and talk with him?"

And so we went. Abraham and Pepe gave each other a long thorough looking over. Then the boy slipped a hand

into Abraham's: "Come, *amigo,* I have something to show."

They left, fast friends, and I wasted no time with Alfredo. "Tell me more about Pepe, please. How did he come to Seville? Is he a relative? And does he really believe he can earn enough selling seeds to buy a burro?"

"He believes, I do not, *señora.* But how can I break that spirit, that pride? I must let him hope for a little while longer, until good fortune comes. Let us all pray it will come." His eyes had brimmed to overflowing and he wiped away many tears, I think, with his old woolen sleeve. Then he went on to tell how Pepe had come. It seemed that a relative of Alfredo's had a farm next to the one Pepe's father worked. Much ill fortune had come to that family — it was sad, and had nearly broken the *papacito.* The boy measured up to more than his years or his frail body. The relative thought in a big city like Seville there would be tourists and opportunity for Pepe to fulfill his great wish — to buy a burro so that the *papacito* might not have to work so hard.

"It is something to break one's heart. And the boy needs so much more than a burro, *señora,* — warm clothes, new, stout shoes to keep his feet off the cold of the pavement. And before all, he needs food, much food to fill a stomach that has gone empty too long."

It was indeed something to break one's heart. But what to do! I still could not see our hurting Pepe's pride by offering him money. What I said to Alfredo was: "We must remember Pepe feels himself almost a man. Let us hope good fortune may come."

They returned, Pepe's hand still holding fast to Abraham's, his face turned upwards and almost radiant. It was as if he had suddenly found a friend and had shared a secret with him. When we started homeward, he was loath to let Abraham go.

As we walked we shared experiences, Abraham and I. Pepe had taken Abraham to a great fir tree whose branches almost swept the ground. They ducked under together and Abraham saw what the boy had done to make a home for himself in Seville. Under the tree had been spread an old mule-blanket. Between two tree roots had been scooped out a deep hole that now held the dead ashes of a last night's fire. With the true courtesy of a *caballero,* Pepe had swept a hand over his domain saying: "This is my *casa.* Now it is yours."

Abraham must have acknowledged this with equal courtesy, for Pepe had gone on with mounting delight: "Alfredo lets me gather all the fagots I need from under the other trees in the park. Every night he brings me my supper. *Café con leche* he brings in a small pot with much bread, sometimes a piece of sausage. It is good. You see, *amigo,* I am most comfortable."

As Abraham talked, I wondered was that coffee-with-milk

and the bread all the lad had to eat throughout the day? Remembering the ample meals we had, my stomach as well as my heart was wrung with shame. What the boy had not told Abraham, for the good reason that he did not know it, was that if the city directors of the park found out that a small boy was camping out under one of the trees and building a fire every night, Alfredo would lose his job. To brush this distressing thought away, I told Abraham all Alfredo had told me. Then, remembering the look on Pepe's face when he and Abraham had joined us, I asked: "What was the secret Pepe shared with you?"

"How did you know there was a secret?"

"Surely he told you one," I said.

Abraham grinned. "He surely did. But how did you know?"

"His face. When you came back his face shone with a great happiness and a great expectancy that was all his own."

Abraham grinned. "There is a secret shared with thousands of children. In two days the Three Kings from the Orient will ride. Pepe has believed, ever since he heard the Kings rode through Seville, that they will bring him a burro for this *papacito* of his. He said it over and over: 'A present it will be, a *regalo* — a big one — because the *papacito* is such a good man.' "

And we had never thought of the Kings! So much could be done in their name. I could have shouted for joy. "Two

days left and not a moment to waste. Two days!" And I hurried Abraham back to our hotel.

That night at dinner, after he had finished his soup, to
my great surprise Abraham suddenly stood up on his chair to
address the tourists in the dining room. In the few days I had
known him I had thought of Abraham as a shy fellow, but I
must have been mistaken. His voice was strong and urgent.
"Many of you are strangers here. Many of you may not remember that on the day after tomorrow, which is Twelfth
Night, the Three Kings will ride. Here in Spain the children
believe he will bring them presents, at least one present. Now
there is at this moment in Seville a very small, ill-fed little boy
who has come from his father's farm in the uplands. That is
a long journey for a small boy. He has come because he
hopes to earn enough money to buy his much-loved *papacito*
a burro. He thinks of himself as almost a man. He doesn't
know — and no one has told him yet — that it will be
months before he can earn enough to buy even an old and de-
crepit burro." Abraham stopped; his lips were dry. He seemed
to be running out of those things he wanted to say. And so
I said softly: "Keep on. Everyone is interested. You are doing
splendidly."

I guess it was the encouragement Abraham needed. His
usually solemn face broke into a smile: "I think you should
know that this little one thinks — he thinks the Three Kings
will bring him a burro to help this *papacito,* who is sick."

Again came a silence. Abraham looked down at me and smiled again. Doggedly he went on: "Perhaps you are thinking just what we have been thinking all day — that because Pepe is a stranger in the city the Three Kings may not know he is here, and so they might not leave that burro that he is hoping for so much. After dinner I am going to pass my hat around. Anything you care to give to help the Three Kings remember this small boy we would greatly appreciate."

Around went the hat. Spanish *pesos,* English crowns and pound notes, American dollars went into it. Afterwards in my room we counted the money and knew that with my portion added there was enough to buy all that was needed.

All through the next day we shopped; stores would be closed on Twelfth Night. We found warm woolen knickers in all sizes and all black. I asked why only black? For a small boy navy or brown or even plaid would be so much gayer. The shopkeeper gave me a puzzled look, then answered: "The *señora* does not know, perhaps, that the poor are always losing some member of the family, always burying someone. In respect for the dead, they must wear black, so black they wear all the time."

So into the pile with the black knickers went warm stockings, strong sturdy shoes — allowing for growth — a heavy woolen blanket to serve as a burro-blanket when Pepe should ride proudly home to the *papacito,* and also as an extra covering at night under the fir tree. We spent some time choosing the jacket. It was the shopkeeper who helped us decide. "You are troubled about the black knickers. Here is a gay jacket, a kind of copy of the jackets the *matadores* wear in the bullring. I think it will please enormously that boy you are buying gifts for."

"These are gifts that the Three Kings bring. I think they would bring just such a jacket to Pepe," I said.

Our last purchase was the burro. Neither of us knew anything about horseflesh, or burro-flesh for that matter. But we tried to act wisely. We felt legs and opened mouths and looked at teeth and found at last a good-tempered, well-fed little creature with every tooth sound in his head. By rare chance, one of the tourists from the hotel came along that moment and he knew a lot about ponies as well as horses. With skillful fingers, he tried legs, turned up hooves, opened the mouth and at last nodded his approval. "That burro is a good buy. He cannot be more than three, four years old." So we bought him and arranged with his former owner to add a bridle and deliver him at midnight the following night at the entrance to the Parque Maria Luisa.

The next day at early noon, the Three Kings rode along the street that bordered the plaza. The plaza filled as if by magic. One moment it held but a scattering of people, but before we knew it it was so crowded one could hardly move or even raise an elbow. Spanish crowds are good-natured and

well-behaved. No one jostled or pushed. We had found a good vantage point at a far corner from where we could see the Kings approaching. I said a Spanish crowd does not jostle, but as we stood still and expectant, we felt a gentle pushing against our knees. Looking down, we saw Pépe. His relief showed as he clasped two eager arms about my knees.

"How did you ever do it?" I asked.

"It was the *señora's* shoes. There were not too many feet wearing American shoes."

"*Hombre,* you are clever. Wait with us and when the Kings come Abraham will lift you to his shoulders where you can see all." I gave a silent prayer that the Kings would come before Pepe smothered down there among everybody's shoes.

Soon we heard the music — haunting minor chords and cadences — played, I think, on old desert instruments. There were ancient viols, flutes and pipes that sounded like the pipes the shepherds play up in the Sierras. The music held an old-world quality. Then we saw the outriders. So closely were we packed that the only way Abraham could get the boy to his shoulders was by turning him about to face him — then, holding both hands, Pepe climbed upwards. With one leg on Abraham's shoulder, he slung the other around his neck. From this height, Pepe's voice rose in triumph: "Truly, I can see everything. And today I sold twenty packets of seeds!"

Each King had his standard-bearer who hailed the crowd with "Hola! Here comes the King." Caspar and Mel-

chior rode white stallions, but Balthazar, the black King, rode
a black stallion. The Kings' robes were gay with colors, heavy
with gold lace and beadwork; their golden crowns were heavy
with jewels. Following each King came a half-dozen burros
with red tassels and bells on their harnesses. Their panniers
were filled with toys. Following these came two two-wheeled
carts drawn by bullocks. These were filled with toys and each
bullock had a wreath gay with flowers and ribbons about
its neck. As each King rode abreast of the crowd, he reached
for a saddlebag and with a wide sweep of the hand scattered
candies to everyone. There were chocolates, caramels and
Turkish paste, all done up in silver and gold papers.

Pepe was quick with his catching. I could hear his happy,
piping voice crying out: "I have caught two. I have caught
many more." And so he had. But it was the burros that
seemed to delight him most. "Just such a one — just such a
burro would make the *papacito* very joyful." And above
Pepe's voice came the shouting of the crowd: *"Magnífico!
Más splendido que nada!"*

We waited for the crowd to scatter; then Abraham put
Pepe back on his feet and gave the boy the most inviting in-
vitation: "Look, *hombre!* This has given a man a big appetite.
Let us find a restaurant with an empty table and fill our empty
stomachs."

We had to search out three cafés before we found a table.
We all had *café con leche* and *pan de gloria,* a delectable sweet

bread; and Pepe had a generous length of hot sausage. There was a plentiful amount of butter and jam to eat with the bread and no one bothered to talk. I marveled at the boy's good manners. Pepe must have been very hungry but not only did he take his food with grace but he stopped suddenly, thrust his hand into the pocket of his knickers and brought out a fistful of candy: "For you. I want you to have some of the Three Kings' sweets." We thanked him but said we had no appetite left, and a half hour later we saw him off to the park. He turned twice to wave us a farewell. He did not know, but we knew we would not be seeing Pepe again.

Abraham gave him a last piece of advice: "Look here, *hombre*. Do you still believe the Kings will bring a burro for the *papacito*? For if you do, remember this. They are wise men as well as Kings and they do not leave even small gifts where boys stay awake watching for them to come."

"I will remember, *amigo*. I will sleep soundly because I believe and because I shall be very tired."

We picked up the burro at midnight outside the park. Abraham had his pocket full of oats, which he fed the burro while I tethered him to a tree just opposite the fir tree where Pepe slept. As quietly as we could, we ducked under that fir's low branches and found a bundle rolled up tightly in the old mule-blanket. Over the bundle we spread the new blanket; then we hung everything on low branches close to the trunk of the tree. Close beside Pepe we laid a cheap leather wallet with enough paper money inside to buy food for boy and burro on their way home. We stood there silently a moment and then, very softly, whispered the farewell all good friends say to those about to set forth on a journey: "*Vaya con Dios, amigo!*"

Two days later, when I went out to the Parque Maria Luisa to feed the birds, Alfredo told me of the boy's departure. Even Alfredo at the last believed that the Three Kings had come: "They brought him everything he needed as well as a fine burro. You should have seen him dressed for the journey. You should have seen him ride away on the burro with all the pride of a man. I shall miss that Pepe, *señora*."

During the rest of my stay in Seville, I went often to the park to feed the birds with Alfredo, but I also missed that scrawny, ill-fed little boy with eyes far too large for his face.

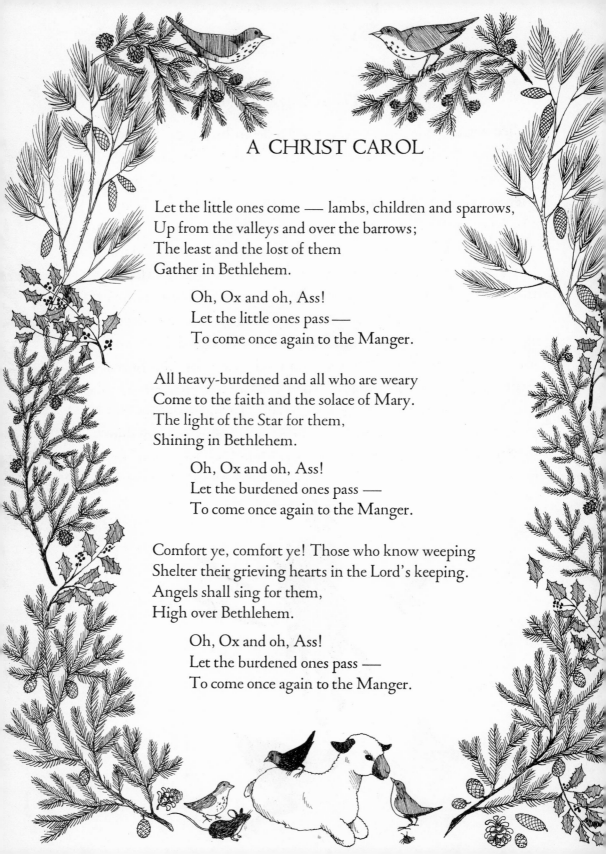

A CHRIST CAROL

Let the little ones come — lambs, children and sparrows,
Up from the valleys and over the barrows;
The least and the lost of them
Gather in Bethlehem.

    Oh, Ox and oh, Ass!
    Let the little ones pass —
    To come once again to the Manger.

All heavy-burdened and all who are weary
Come to the faith and the solace of Mary.
The light of the Star for them,
Shining in Bethlehem.

    Oh, Ox and oh, Ass!
    Let the burdened ones pass —
    To come once again to the Manger.

Comfort ye, comfort ye! Those who know weeping
Shelter their grieving hearts in the Lord's keeping.
Angels shall sing for them,
High over Bethlehem.

    Oh, Ox and oh, Ass!
    Let the burdened ones pass —
    To come once again to the Manger.

Let the meek and the pure in heart come, and the lowly;
These are the blessed ones, these are the holy.
Incense and myrrh for them,
Waiteth in Bethlehem.

    Oh, Ox and oh, Ass!
    Let the blessed ones pass —
    All hallow them here at the Manger.

God is forever the God of the living;
He giveth His Son in perpetual giving.
All nations kneel to him,
Reborn in Bethlehem.

    Oh, Ox and oh, Ass!
    Let the dying world pass —
    And Peace be proclaimed at the Manger.

San Froilan of the Wilderness

An Old Spanish Legend

ONE MUST USUALLY dig for old legends or else come by them by happy chance. It was by chance that I was in Galicia in northern Spain. There I happened on a small chapel standing on the fringe of the wilderness. It was built of stone and looked like hundreds of others scattered throughout Spain; that is, from the outside. Inside, it was different. Over the altar there was a *retablo* of stone — one solid slab. It looked like common stone, roughly hewn. There were two figures, one of a pilgrim monk and one of a wolf. The caretaker, or *sacristán,* saw my interest. "There is a true story about those two. Would the *señora* like to hear it?"

The *sacristán* had little notion of time. "How long ago was the chapel built? When did the pilgrim monk come to the wilderness? Did he follow the good Santiago?" The old man shook his head. What did it matter?

Brother Froilan came into the wilderness with few worldly

possessions. He carried across his shoulders an old rug for coverage. Within it were wrapped a hammered brass pot, some few packets of healing herbs, and seeds for growing. His habit was warm, well woven. Around his waist was knotted the cord from which hung his crucifix, and in the knot was a short, well-tempered Damascan blade. In his hands he carried, for the most part, what might have been later called a breviary. It was a small black book, carefully written and most beautifully illuminated with bright letters. It held the story of Christmas and some of the life and teachings of Jesus, the Christ. It held likewise a few psalms and something of the lives of the early apostles.

Brother Froilan had come by sea and had walked those many weary, lonely miles from the landing-port on the west coast. All about him were the remnants of the Germanic tribes, descendants mostly from the West Goths, and all pagans — believing in gods of wood, stone, and sacrifice.

With his good steel blade he built a hut; from the nearby stream he found good clay for an adobe fireplace and chimney in one corner. For long hours during the night he trampled his floor hard and enduring with his bare feet. He had not come without the gift of a few gold pieces, and with one he bought a small gray donkey. This became his companion and friend as well as his beast of burden. He shared with the donkey his meager fare and much that the small black book held. And he found comfort in speech with something living.

In the wilderness about him were many huts holding families, all hostile to the newcomer who could not speak their tongue. All the faces he met held fear and distrust; only the children welcomed him. But these barbarians who shared a part of the wilderness with him had certain laws of hospitality. When he came to their doors, they allowed him to enter, gestured him to a stool by the fire, and even shared their meat with him. But the children gathered close around him with little chirrups of delight, for he had found a way to their hearts. He would sit, pick out a piece of the wood that lay beside the fire, and, taking his good knife, would carve some small beast that they knew — a goat, a calf, a sheep, even a wolf or fox. They had no playthings except for the crude dolls the little girls made for themselves out of the pine cones.

Brother Froilan had not been in the wilderness a year before he had gained the love of all the small ones, and even the elders accepted him with less distrust. He seemed harmless and of good intention. With the gathering in of their language he began to share with them the story of Christmas and some of the teachings of Jesus. They liked best the rhythm of the psalms which the monk read in Latin. They made a pretense of listening to him when he tried to tell them of his God — an Almighty God and a loving father to all. Month after month he toiled with them; in the end he knew it was as though they had not heard him.

These wild folk truly worshiped the sun that gave them warmth and light, the rain that made their wheat to grow, the gentle seasons that brought them well-being and hope. They made sacrifices to fire, wind, and frost; and above all they feared the mysterious being who could slay them with pestilence or wreck their homes and plantings with storm and lightnings. The Christian God meant nothing to them. He remained as strange as the pilgrim monk who had come to dwell among them. Of one thing Brother Froilan was certain: the children loved him and cherished the small beasts he had carved for them.

Through the long second year that he dwelt among them, he thought long on these things. Wherein lay his failure? Wherein lay a hidden meaning in the children's delight in the carven beasts? He talked the matter over often with the donkey: "Brother Burro, what think you? Is it because the small beasts I have made can be held in the hand, because they can be touched and seen? Do things such as these that can be felt and seen stay with one better than words? Things remain — today, tomorrow, and through many tomorrows. They linger in the mind and heart. But words can be soon forgotten. Perchance, this is a truth. We must in some way reach children and untutored wild folk through those things they can handle, hold, possess with their eyes and then with their hearts." He paused the while he thought; and then in deep despair he cried, "But how — how, Brother Burro, do I bring

to these, my chosen people, a knowledge of a loving God through a poorly carved lamb or wolf!"

A third winter of hardship passed, and then came a burgeoning spring. All about the small clearing growing things sprang into leaf and flower. Life came full-toll to the wilderness. Brother Froilan marked with a rising heart the wondrous gift of life he shared. Birds nested under his eaves and in the nearby bush. They wakened him with their joyful matin song. Small brown hares watched him plant his seeds; does with their fawns fed on the roots of bracken and tender grass. Often they licked a gift of dried wheat from his hand. Life! If only he could make the wild folk feel this life as a gift from God! But how?

The answer came to him as all true answers must — out of a quiet mind. Was not the lowly birth of Jesus the greatest gift of life God had ever given the world? And was his birth not only a gift but a symbol? Over and over he had read from his small black book; over and over he had told of the Christmas. And all for naught. Now he must reach them through what all could see, touch, feel; he must teach them by the means of the little beasts he had carved for the children. These had all had a part in that first Christmas. Perchance he could add to them a carving of angels, of shepherds, of kings from the East. And when his hand grew more skillful, he perchance could make a Holy Family. Could he bring such a Christmas to his wild folk, that they would never forget?

As was his wont, he took the donkey into his confidence
and hope. "We will hunt carefully for the right wood to
make everything. The grain must be gentle and the wood
not too hard, not too soft. We will peel off the bark and set
it in the good spring sun to dry. So will it soak into itself all
this gift of new life. It will add a kind of blessing to the carving." Thus went the days of early spring.

The children soon discovered Brother Froilan sitting on his
doorstep, busy with wood and blade. They gathered round
him, watching, asking, "Is that donkey for me?" "Are you
making something wonderful with these little beasts?"

The face of the kindly Brother glowed when he made
answer. "Yes, there is something I need the small beasts for.
I am going to tell a story with them, the most wonderful story
ever told. There will be more than the beasts. You shall
see."

And so never a day passed that some child did not come to
watch, to mark how small beasts could tell a story. Brother
Froilan told it piecemeal, thus: "You see, the donkey must
be in the story, for he brought Mary to Bethlehem. You will
hear about Mary later. And we must have the gentle kine,
for they gave up their manger to the small Jesus. You will
hear about him, too. The shepherds brought their smallest
lambs to him; so, we must have many lambs to tell the story
aright. And on the night that Jesus was born, a splendid star
shone in the sky. Later, I will make the star. And angels sang

a kind of psalm: they sang of peace, good will, and told about
the baby's birth."

As Brother Froilan's hands became more skillful, he began
to carve the shepherds and the angels. So great was the delight
of the children in watching the story take form — not just in
words, but in things coming to life beneath the Brother's
knife — that they shared their delight with their elders.

As the summer waxed and waned, the wild folk came on
days of rain and sat inside the hut and watched the story grow.
For the first time they listened and cherished what they heard.
More than this, they asked questions. "Where was this place
called Bethlehem — far away or near at hand?" "What sort of
creature was an angel — a bird, for it had wings?" "And was
the star that shone that night brighter than the stars that shoot
across the sky in midsummer?"

As the Brother answered the questions, he wove more of
the story for his listeners; then with matching eagerness he
passed from hand to hand the figures he had finished. His
gentle smile gathered all into the wonder of the story, and
always he would finish the same way, "But you must wait and
see it completed — a living story. Watch for it the eve of
Christmas. You will each of you have a manger where two
wood paths cross. Watch for it; then you will understand."

The children took Brother Froilan into the deeper woods
to help him find stains for the figures. They gathered roots,
berries, sometimes the small toadstools, and what they called

"lantern moss," which held at the tip of each green spear a tiny drop of deep crimson. With these the Brother stained Mary's robe a heavenly blue, Joseph's robe a warm brown, and the kings' robes crimson, green, and yellow. With loving dedication Brother Froilan handed each finished figure to a child to be placed with care upon the shelves he had built, the children counting as they did so. "Good Brother, we now have ten shepherds, more kings than we have fingers to count on, and eight angels. So many of everything."

They took less interest in the rough stable that was hewn of tiny logs, the bark left on, with the floors and uprights to hold all together. These had little to tell them; it was the shepherds, the beasts, the kings, and the Holy Families that made the story of Christmas live for them. These were real.

Then came the time of frost. Snapping cold bit at all who ventured far from their fires. Brother Froilan spoke urgently to the gray donkey. "Brother Burro, we must make haste. The Christmastide draws near. We will have much traveling to do to reach all the crosspaths in the wilderness. Every manger must be set up with care, for each must be cherished and understood by all who dwell near it." He clasped his hands: it might have been in prayer or ecstasy. "Think — think, Brother Burro, what it will mean to have a living Christmas! Then truly, God will dwell among us. We will get the baskets packed tonight. Tomorrow we begin."

Brother Froilan had gathered many lengths of delicate

deer-thong to use for binding. No one knew of such things as nails and hammers in that wilderness and in those far-off, ancient days. The gray donkey was heavily burdened with his full baskets; one of them held only the small figures, placed carefully on layers of wood moss so that none should be broken. The wild folk spread deep into the woods and in all directions. The two traveled towards the sun and found the farthest crosspath. There the long-patient pilgrim monk began the fulfillment of his years in the wilderness. He worked with care. He chose two straight saplings growing close together by the crosspaths. These he cut evenly, waist-high from the ground. He bound them to afford a firm foundation for the floor of a manger. This he fastened securely and level. Thereupon he placed an upright in each corner, and on these he fitted the slanting roof — slanting that it might shed rain or snow. On a slender twig above the roof he fashioned a star, and on either side an angel. These were the heavenly host that sang "Gloria in excelsis." These were the ones who brought God's message of "Peace on earth, good will to men!" How many times he had spoken this message to the wild folk of the wilderness. Now they would see it being proclaimed and believe at last.

With his arm about the donkey he spoke many words of wonder as he set the Holy Family within the stable, the beasts and shepherds and kings in their appointed places. "See, Brother Burro, our Mary kneels close to the manger. We cover the small Jesus with the small spread the children made for him. He sleeps warm and safe. Now we place the lowly cattle — a goat here, the donkey there. At the threshold we bring the shepherds with their lambs to worship Him. And that all may know the kings came later, we will put them farther away, but being guided by the star. It is finished, our story of Christmas." Brother Froilan sighed with deep thankfulness. He gave the donkey a final pat. "You have been a faithful servant — not only to me but to the good God who watches over us."

Those last days before Christmas went on swift feet. Together Brother and burro worked throughout the short winter days, reaching their hut at dusk, footsore but content. And, for the first time, the wild folk brought offerings of meat and fish caught through the ice and laid them on his rough-hewn table that he might have strengthening food for his evening meal. To Brother Froilan it seemed as if his heart could not hold the full of his thankfulness.

Christmas Eve broke clear, but the coldest of all the winter days. There were left but two mangers to carry, and these to far-off wood paths lying northwards. Brother and burro waited until the sun should bring some warmth to the ground and comfort for their bodies; it was close to the noontide before they were finally packed and off. The woods about them seemed strangely still. Every twig snapped beneath their feet, sounding with a loudness almost frightening. Many times

the donkey stopped and shivered; and, before they had reached the first crosspath, he had picked up a sharp stone in his hoof. Carefully Brother Froilan dug it out with his knife, but it left his faithful donkey limping grievously as he followed.

The Brother worked clumsily and slowly, his fingers stiff from the cold. He fumbled making the knots in the deer-thong. He dropped many of the small figures setting them in place. In the wood-silence he stopped often to listen, thinking he heard the sound of wild creatures moving in the brush. With the manger in place he looked overhead to mark the rapid sinking of the winter sun. He must make more haste if he and his faithful companion would reach their hut before darkness.

The next crosspath lay more than a kilometer's distance; and they could not hasten, for the lameness in Brother Burro's hoof had worsened. The Brother knew this part of the wilderness. Thus, when they had reached a small valley with the last crosspath laying some distance up a rough slope, he tethered the donkey there. Unpacking the last manger, he carried the many pieces in a fold in his cloak and scrambled hot-foot upwards. Again he worked clumsily, his hands chilled through. Everything he handled was cold, and already dusk was gathering before the last of the kings was placed.

Even then Brother Froilan was loath to leave. He spoke softly to his handiwork. "Stand strong and true against the

night. Speak your story clearly when the Christmas sun shines. Speak it to the wild folk who pass, to the children who come to mark, even to the wild creatures who pass this way. I have heard that the wild creatures know this holy night. Pray God there may be some who come to kneel before the small Jesus. Thou hast been sent to teach the world the meaning of life, of eternal love, of peace, and brotherhood."

It was with renewed thankfulness and devotion that the Brother stumbled his way back to where he had left the donkey. Often he was forced to stop for breath. Suddenly, the wood-silence around him was broken, and he heard carried on the night wind the ominous sound of snarls and throaty growls. Before he could gather up his robe again and hasten downward, there came another sound that filled his heart with fear. It was the feeble braying of a donkey. Tearing the heavy brush apart, he plunged on until he came to the small valley where he had tethered Brother Burro. What he beheld filled him with shock and anger. His hand reached quickly for the blade at his waist.

Not a dozen feet from where he stood crouched a great, ravenous wolf, his fangs bared. Never had the eyes of man and beast met with such fierce enmity. The wolf crouched ready to spring; Brother Froilan's hand readied to plunge his knife into the heart of the murderous beast. From where he stood, he could see all too plainly what lay at the wolf's feet. Tethered, the gray donkey had not had the smallest chance to save himself. Anger at the beast who had slain his burro changed on the moment to anger against himself. He alone was to blame for this. Slowly his arm sank; slowly the knife was thrust again into the cord at his waist. Then, holding out both hands, he spoke with the stern voice of the avenger, "Brother Wolf, come to me!"

The wolf stayed, unmoving. In truth, it is doubtful if he had ever heard a human voice before. And it is ever the way of a creature, tame or wild, to listen when man speaks. Dusk and wood-silence folded them in. No sound passed between the two. But now, the eyes of Brother Froilan held no anger, only a command. Slowly, half crawling, the wolf obeyed. He reached the Brother's feet and laid his great head on a sandal, his eyes no longer fearful, but pleading. When the holy man spoke again, his voice had gentled. "So, Brother Wolf, you were hungry. You killed that you might eat. I fear that is the custom of both man and beast. But God made a commandment: 'Thou shalt not kill!' and you have killed a faithful beast, a good servant to God and myself. It is therefore fitting that you should do penance. Come! Henceforth, you shall be my beast of burden and my companion."

The wolf got to his feet. Patiently he waited while Brother Froilan undid the saddle cloth on the donkey and lifted the baskets, placing them securely on the wolf's back. With a hand on the great head, Brother Froilan led the way back to his hut. He shared his meal with the wolf; and later, when he

laid himself down on his hard pallet, the wolf stretched out by the fire. All through that long night, whenever the Brother rose to throw more wood upon the fire, the wolf reached out a cleansed tongue and licked his master's bare feet. Without more words between them, Brother Wolf accepted the penance put upon him — he would serve both God and man.

In spite of the grievous loss of the gray donkey, it was a joyous Christmas. The day was filled with wonder of children and wild folk: wonder at the story told by each manger, but wonder, too, at the coming of a wolf — a beast they feared most in the wilderness — to learn the gentle, kindly ways of the holy man who had come to dwell among them. And there was wonder in the heart of Brother Froilan as well, that now he could go back to his small black book and teach and tell all that it held; and the ears of the wilderness were now eager to listen and to comprehend. Wherever he wandered, Brother Froilan was made welcome. Brother Wolf was given a place beside the fires. The smallest children played with him; and, when cold and drowsiness overtook them, they huddled close to his warm fur and slept.

In the years that followed, it seemed as if God's blessing had fallen on the wilderness. The wild folk, learning it was the custom of Christians to build a place of worship, made a clearing near Brother Froilan's hut. Hither they fetched stone and clay and built a chapel according to his directions. A great cross, hewn out of oak, crowned the ridgepole. Many of the faraway dwellers moved near to the chapel. And every Christmas Eve the mangers were again placed at the cross-paths for all to wonder at and cherish. So there came at last a fulfillment of Brother Froilan's mission.

They died on the same day, the two, Brother Froilan and Brother Wolf. Their people dug a common grave for them near the chapel, wrapping the holy man in his robe and the beast in one of their crude-woven rugs.

How many centuries ago? The *sacristán* did not know — and did it matter? "You see, *señora,* they have rested well together. The name of the stonecutter who made the *retablo* is forgotten, but it keeps for us their memory. And after many years Brother Froilan was sainted in Rome. That is why we now remember him as San Froilan of the Wilderness."

A FRAGMENT FROM A LATIN CAROL

Come tell your beads while bells are ringing,
Tune your ears to angels' singing,
Open hearts to thankful giving
    On this, the Christmas Day.

Hail, sweet Mary, come and bless us,
And thou, O Lord, our sins confess us;
And may no evil deed distress us
    On this, the Christmas Day.

To others' faults let there be blindness,
To others' speech keep open-mindness,
And to all neighbors — acts of kindness
    On this, the Christmas Day.

The Miracle of Saint Cumgall

A Legend of a Lost Saint

THERE WERE FIVE of them just — holy friars all of them. They tramped the length of Ireland to see a dream come true. Four of them were built big men, sturdy and straight; their eyes could look, unflinching, into the sun and their hands could raise a weight of ten stone. Aye, strong they were. But the fifth was cut from another pattern. He was a smallish man, thin as a whipcord. His face was gentle — to match the voice he had.

There was no telling from what country they had come — these five — but they told their beads in good Latin and a soft Gaelic slipped easily from their tongue. Their black woolen robes were as thick as a lamb's fleece — fit to keep out the cold of winter or the heat of summer. Each carried a heavy bundle strapped well across his shoulders. What they held who can be telling? They held what was needed for the day and the morrow — aye, and for the fulfillment of their dream.

Under their habits were slung pouches, each holding a bit of Roman gold, and along with that what to them was richer than gold — sheets of parchment, some carrying words, brightly made, some empty, waiting to hold the record of their dream.

From the beginning of their journey they had chosen the smallish one to be their leader — Brother Cumgall they called him. For all the gentleness that was his they knew the strength that lay within him and the will, linked to God's own, that would stand firm under all hardships. 'Twas this strength and will that outlasted all that the four sturdy Brothers could stand. When their spirits weakened it was Brother Cumgall who had words of cheer to urge them on. His voice never chastened them, but when their bones ached and the soles of their feet cried out for rest, it was the smallish friar who broke into a merry tune — fitting words to it — that would carry them a few furlongs further at day's end. What Brother Cumgall said went somewhat in this wise:

> Follow, Brothers, follow, follow —
> Up yonder hill — down yonder hollow —
> Strong as ox and free as swallow —
> Follow, Brothers, follow.
>
> Bless the earth for feeding us
> Bless wind and sun for heeding us
> Bless the good God for leading us —
> Follow, Brothers, follow.

The four sturdy ones talked much among themselves, but Brother Cumgall walked silently, keeping all that he might be thinking to himself. Only upon those times when he spied a bird on a nearby bush, or a small brown hare taking cover in a wood-copse, did speech come freely. "God's greeting to you, Brother Throstle," he would cry, "can you tell us where we may find food to fill five empty bellies? And is aught of danger ahead?"

And then would follow much twittering and chirping, and when it came to an end Brother Cumgall would speak to the others: "Brothers, ahead lies no danger — and for food a meadow full of whortleberries and a stream full of graylings." He would leave much thankfulness behind with the bird and set a smarter pace towards stream and meadow. And come the morrow it would be the brown hare he would inquire of: "Brother Hare — what sort of land and folk lie ahead?" So softly given was the answer that the four listeners wondered did he speak at all; but the look of troubled awareness that showed on Brother Cumgall's face prepared them for the spoken words: "We are told to keep far from the sea. Fierce and unholy men live there. They fall upon wayfarers; and they hate the sight of cassock or cowl."

Often the four would have asked Brother Cumgall how had it come about that he should know the speech of the wild creatures but they never dared ask. So passed the seasons until there came a day when they found beyond the crest of

hill a small lough or pond, and on the waters of the lough swam a dun-colored duck with a band of green upon throat and wings. Brother Cumgall reached for the crumbs of oaten-bread he always had with him and called: "Brother Duck — I would have speech with thee." The duck swam to the narrow beach, waddled out, shook water from his wings and came up to the kneeling friar who waited until his hand was empty of bread. Then he asked: "We have journeyed through four seasons and over much rough land. We are seeking a fitting place to build a monastery. If the land is free here-abouts perchance you can tell us how near the sea it is — where lie good pasturage and meadows for planting wheat and barley?"

There followed such a quacking as the four Brothers had never heard. They listened, understanding none of it but read-ing easily the changes that showed in Brother Cumgall's face. Eagerness was there — surprise — a quiet sense of fulfillment. At the end the smallish Brother threw himself down beside the four. "God be praised — 'Tis a grand ending we have to our long journey. Over yonder hill lies the sea. Over the hill beyond lie woodlands, between us and the sea stretch good meadows, between the two hills lies pasturage. The land is free for the taking. God be praised."

The four echoed his last words: "God be praised!" and so was the beginning made of the first monastery built in the north of Ireland.

The Brother who became cook also became the gatherer of food — cockles from the beach, dillisk at low water for the making of puddings, honey from the wild bees, salmon from the stream's mouth where they mounted to go up and spawn — and so it went. The next Brother became the planter of grain and green things and the gatherer of good herbs. The two strongest of the holy men became the builders, while Brother Cumgall started the keeping of records and accounts. Into his keeping was given the small bags of Roman gold to purchase sheep, kine and a small donkey to carry loads. All things prospered. At the end of the first year the kine had multiplied. There had been many lambs. The harvest of wheat and barley had been plentiful and all things prospered.

"Now, good Brothers, we can bring our dream to pass — the founding of a school for Irish lads. I have heard, as you must, that the chieftains are rough, uncouth men. It is time that learning was brought to their homes. Someday this will be a fine, fair part of Ireland — this land of Ulster. Four of us will fare forth and tell of our school; the fifth will mind the monastery. Soon there will be other holy men joining us. We must build swiftly and wisely. Come — let us draw lots and see which of us five shall go."

So was the school started. First with a score of brawny lads, untutored and undisciplined. Each year the number grew. Each year more friars joined the five. At long last they knew there must be an abbot consecrated to the work. United and wholeheartedly they chose Brother Cumgall, and with simple ritual and God's blessing he was ordained.

Mornings were for work. Even the lads took over their share of the plantings: the sheepshearing, the cheese-making, the gathering of berries and cockles, the catching of fish. Afternoons came lessons; and at night Father Cumgall went to his cell to write up the list of earnings and of spendings for the day. At midnight a Brother would bring him a small dole of bread and cheese and milk. As the hour grew late Brother Cumgall would look expectantly towards a small hole in the corner which with nimble fingers he had cautiously enlarged. He looked and he ate sparingly of his dole of food until he saw a small bewhiskered nose thrust through the hole followed by the tidy body of a field mouse with white tips to his tail and all four paws. Outside the hole the mouse waited always for the Father's greeting: "You are most welcome, Brother Mouse. Come share my cheese and bread." Whereupon there would be a quick scampering of small feet, and in a trice Brother Mouse was climbing up the folds of Father Cumgall's habit and perching himself upon the bony knees of the holy Abbot. There would be a fair sharing of the food — a crumb each of bread and cheese for Brother Mouse, a goodly bit for the tired Father. Then speech began between them: "I am tired of figures — my eyes swim with digits. Come tell me, Brother Mouse, what news is abroad?"

There would follow a good recounting of happenings, not

only in Ulster but from three other tenures of Ireland; and sometimes from Tara, the seat of the High King. Open fairs would be held, some nearby, some far away, for the selling and buying of kine, sheep and all beasts of burden. There would be fierce tales of thieving between Ulster and Munster — the stealing of cattle — and more often, the stealing of young wives of other chieftains. Some news touched closely upon the doings at the monastery — concerning as it did the families of some of the school lads. Also when some faraway mice brought in a report that wheat was scarce in the south and a good price was being paid for good grain — then would Father Cumgall dispatch a pair of friars with a two-wheeled cart loaded with wheat. Sometimes the payment would be in calves, or good honey — some in sides of bacon, well smoked; sometimes it was in Roman gold.

The chieftains' sons did well at the abbey. They took to their lessons, even to the strange Latin. But the best of the day's happening was when their small, gentle Abbot took them afield to seek out and learn the names of healing herbs and where they grew — or hunted for the many berries to pick and add much flavor to their simple meals. But best of all was their listening to Father Cumgall talking to the wild folk — hare and fox, weasel and bird. As one lad said, "The wild things love and honor him even as we do," and so it was in truth.

On one of these walks with his lads came a sudden end to

the prospering of all their efforts. On their way back from a
fine picking of gooseberries that Father Cumgall promised
should be made into tarts for their tea, they came upon two
strange and new visitors to the lough. They were a pair of
white swans — never before seen in the north of Ireland. The
lads huddled in great excitement as Father Cumgall walked
to the small beach and scattered bits of bread upon the waters.
One swan swam towards him making a low, trumpeting
sound that the good Abbot found strange to his ears: "You
are welcome, Brother Swan. You tell me you have flown this
way — going south — to bring me a message. I hope it
promises to be a hopeful message."

The swan's low trumpeting went unbroken for a lee long
time. The lads watching saw the Abbot's gentle face change
from delight to despair. Not until the swans took flight did
he turn to his lads, and sadly he spoke. "Let ye harken well,
for this message belongs to you as it does to me and everyone
who has at heart the good work of the Monastery. That swan
brought a message from my wild friends from everywhere
over the land. This will be the last harvest we will have for
many a long time. A terrible drought will come with the
spring. All planted things will die — even grass will be unfit
to feed our sheep, our cattle, our mules and donkeys. We will
know great want and hunger." He turned homeward: "This
will be bitter news to share along with your gooseberry tarts,
lads."

The four Brothers who had taken the journey throughout the length of Ireland with their Abbot so many years before met in Father Cumgall's cell for a conclave. It was agreed that all within the abbey should be told of the message — that all might well understand why ropes should be tighter drawn around stout bellies and too-eager appetites must be curbed. They would harvest with a greater care; while the cows still gave milk aplenty, extra cheese should be made. It would be best to slaughter all the pigs, for hams and bacon and chitterlings could be well kept.

It was well after midnight that the Abbot spoke his final words. "We must warn all the countryside of this coming drought, that they may prepare wisely, chieftains and farmers alike. No school for the next few days. We will send each lad back to his own family with an urgent warning to plan frugally for the years ahead."

So the lads were dispatched, but they were met with scant belief. Ulster had never suffered a drought; Ireland had never had a famine. They had brought words of nonsense from their Abbot with due respect to the calling. And when by chance some curious one asked whence came this warning of drought and famine and the lad questioned told that a white swan had brought the message to their abbot, a burst of raucous laughter and scorn filled the hall where all had gathered to welcome their chieftain's son. What decent Ulsterman would heed the warning of a nitwit abbot! There would be time enough when the spring rains failed and the grain withered to take heed.

Each season that passed confirmed the white swan's message. At the end of the first year it was the chieftains who sent each a messenger to Father Cumgall: would the good Abbot keep the lads and feed them through the coming year? By that time surely the drought would be broken and there would be plenty again. But for the present each chieftain had scarcely enough to feed their fighting men — much less a parcel of young, untried lads.

The Abbot listened to each messenger in turn, a quiet smile on his face. Each he sent back with the same answer: "So long as we have food in our storehouses the lads shall be fed." He might have added what he had already told the friars: "We have a portion of Young Ireland to protect. It matters little if we go hungry; the lads must have enough to grow on — to keep up their courage and their faith."

No rains fell. That second spring the run of salmon failed. The lads and friars searched up and down the beaches for cockles and dillisk until none was left. The streams and lough were empty of fish. The cows grew hollow-bellied and gave no milk; the beasts of burden starved. Of one thing only there was plenty — the boglands gave all the peat the Brothers could cut and carry to keep fires burning against the cold.

But a fresh, unbidden want knocked at the door of the Monastery and cried for help. The King of Ulster's son —

the cruel ne'er-do-well — had descended upon the barns and storehouses of all farmers and serfs and picked them clean of flour, cheese and meat. Their children were dying slowly. Surely the holy Brothers could spare a little of their plenty.

And spare they did — though little it was. But the time came when the door was bolted and the only help the Brothers could give was the last sacrament to the dying and burial for the dead.

Long before this time came Father Cumgall had shared his last dole of bread and cheese with Brother Mouse. Sad-eyed, he watched the whiskered nose poke itself out. Never had his voice spoken so gentle a welcome.

"Welcome as always, Brother Mouse, but 'tis the last dole we will be sharing." There was a scampering of feet across the hard-packed floor, a hurried climbing of white-tipped feet up the worn habit. The Abbot looked down sadly at his small friend: "No more accounts to keep, Brother Mouse. No longer is there aught to sell, no longer aught to buy. One has no need of figures when the ground lies parched and every wind that blows carries the cry of hunger." A thin, well-wrinkled hand cupped itself around the mouse while another hand held out the waiting crumb of cheese.

Then did Brother Mouse make his troubled answer: "I cannot take of your dole, Father Abbot, unless you share it with me." So in silence the small crumbs were divided between them. Then did Father Cumgall speak again: "Brother

Mouse, before you go your ways and leave me to go mine I would know how fares all your kin in Ulster. Is there still food for them?"

"Such as it is there is enough. We have gathered thriftily — dry roots to gnaw, seeds of grasses and from the dropped cones in the woods nearby. It is scanty fare but we will last through till rains fall and there is new life again upon this famined earth."

"Take my blessing to all your kind — to all the small folk. Tell them they have gathered more wisely than the human folk. Tell them I wish there might be aught to share with them."

Brother Mouse nuzzled for a small moment the withered hand that cupped him. "The blessing will serve us well — we will survive," and with a sudden flick of tail and ears the mouse was gone.

For months now the gaunt figures of the Brothers moved about the abbey, on ever-slowing feet, fulfilling what tasks they could as best they could. The Abbot missed the midnight visits of his small friend more than he would let himself believe. The only thing that stirred the hearts of the Brotherhood to a waking hope each day was the lasting strength and faithfulness of the lads. As yet hunger had not bitten in too deeply to mark its ravages on their youth and strength. Father Cumgall well remembered how in the early days of the school, these sons of chieftains had leaned too heavily on the strength and faith of himself and the sturdy friars; now, the friars were leaning on the lads — not only for the hope to bring them through but on the faith and good cheer of these same lads.

One day, winter having come, Father Cumgall went to the cellar and storerooms to count what remained of food to carry them through to another spring. Brother Cook went with him. They stood together outside the door of the last storehouse and shook a pair of sorrowful heads, bowed with defeat. "If we eat but twice each day — a thin broth and small bread after matins, and whatever you can devise before evensong — how long will food last us?"

It took but a moment for Brother Cook to make reply: "Barely until the Christmastide. After that — nothing."

Returning to the Abbot's cell, they talked softly, trying to devise some plan that might add to their scanty store. "It will take a miracle. The whole of Ulster starves. There is no source of nourishment left — nothing we have not tried," said Brother Cook.

"A miracle! Truly. Let us remember that Christ fed a multitude on a few loaves and fishes. He also performed the miracle of changing the hearts of sinners and cruel men. There is one source of help we have not sought. It has been in my mind of late but I have been loath to try it." Brother Cook looked long at his superior and nodded: "I think I guess the source, but like yourself I should be loath to try it."

The words Father Cumgall then spoke were few. "Nevertheless, I go. With God's blessing and Christ's help I will try to change the heart of a greedy, cruel man. Say naught to the others. I leave at daybreak."

So did Father Cumgall start on the long, rough journey to the castle of the King of Ulster's son. His worn woolen robe was wrapped tight about his thin body, his cowl was pulled down to meet his eyes and shield as best it could the sharpness of the winter wind. To feed him and keep up his strength he had brought but the smallest dole — counting at least on unfailing Irish hospitality to offer him a good meal at the end of his journey. He slept a little, where he could find shelter; he pecked like a small bird at the crumbs of bread and cheese his pouch held. He lost all track of days, noting only that the sun was high overhead when the stone turrets of the castle towered ahead.

A surly chieftain led him into the great feasting hall that stretched the length of the castle. Before the Abbot could gather his wits or steady his much-weakened body a coarse, ringing laugh shook the rafters and a cruel voice followed it: "What ho there! Can I believe my eyes! Do I see a man of God come staggering into my great hall? And what a ragged man of God!" Again came the laughter, then, with a sudden taunting soberness, "Tell me — what can the King's son give you that your God cannot?"

The speech finished, the King's son returned to his eating.

The long table, raised above the common folk, was well spread with venison, young pig, pastries and fresh loaves of bread, cheese and wine and tarts — enough to feed an army. As Father Cumgall's watery eyes cleared from the long cold he had suffered, he marked the well-spread table — the first he had seen since the beginning of the drought. So stiff was his tongue that words came with difficulty. When he spoke he wondered would his voice carry across the hall.

"King's son, I have come to ask you to share your plenty with those who are starving. We need food at the Abbey — not for ourselves but to feed the sons of chieftains, given into our care. If they survive this famine, they may serve you well in years to come."

Again the rafters shook with laughter. "So you come abegging — man of God. I find this mighty humorous. Let the chieftains feed their own sons — I give no food to those who do not now serve me. Nor do I like too well to have beggars share my hall while I sit at meat. Fellows — put this man of God out!"

A dozen burly fellows came, but not one laid hand on Father Cumgall. He was speaking again, his voice gathering strength: "For a year now you have stolen food from the weaker, poorer people of Ulster. Those who could not stand against you we have tried to feed, until autumn has come and our own storehouses are empty. Hearken well, oh King's son. In truth I come abegging to ask your help in feeding the youth of Ireland, lest they lose their faith — both in man-kind and God. This is the Christmas season, the time when all bring gifts to the child in Bethlehem. Laugh if you must at a man of God who comes in rags abegging; but do not laugh — I warn you — at the day we soon keep, the birthday of our Lord."

A terrible silence fell upon all in the great hall. For a long moment food and feasting were forgotten and faces turned towards the King's son with fear and anger. The abbot never knew whether the greedy man who sat at meat wished he might take back the cruel words he had spoken or whether he was choking on the piece of venison he had but then stuffed into his mouth. When he spoke it was without laughter or scorn. "Fellows — put this whining man of God without. I have had enough of him."

With a wisp of hope hugged close to his heart, the long, hard trip to the castle had kept the Abbot's feet dragging one after another. Now, with hunger gnawing the last of his strength, he held no thought of ever reaching the abbey again. No memory of the days he spent upon the journey homeward remained with him. He was as a man already dead when Brother Cook, watching for his return, ran out the door and far into the snow to half carry, half drag the unconscious Abbot inside. A warm fire burned in the refectory and Father Cumgall lay there through two nights and a day without stirring. Brother Cook told in fragments what had been his mission — and what must have been the outcome. "Let no one question the good Father when he awakens. Then let what wine there is left be given him. Until then let all of us spend as much time as we have from our tasks in prayer and thanksgiving."

As for Father Cumgall, through those long hours his mind was muddled with strange dreams. Small field mice scampered in and out of them, a few wild creatures who had survived the famine followed the mice: a pair of wild boars, a buck and a doe, foxes and brown hares, all muddled up with the field mice, scampering around him. It was the day before Christmas before he came to himself, drank some of the wine that was held to his lips and asked to be helped to his cell, where he wished to be left alone and undisturbed till evensong.

No one ate that day — not a morsel of food remained. All within the abbey thanked God for the warmth of good fires as they looked abroad at the heavy covering of snow that lay over the land. At midnight Father Cumgall walked unaided to the chapel and said the Christmas Mass. Before the benediction he held up a shaking hand. "You will go to your cells and give thanks to God that again the Holy Babe is born in Bethlehem. Remember there was no room for Mary and Joseph at the inn. Only the creatures gave of their manger — a place for Him to lie. Remember — being the poorest of folk there was probably no food for them this night. And yet, throughout the night a star of great promise shined upon them and angels sang of goodwill among all men."

They slept the night through, and who can say there was
not some hope in the hearts of all when Father Cumgall spoke
again at Matins: "We have served God humbly and lovingly.
We have fed the needy, blessed all creatures. Let us finish by
giving thanks that we have all been spared to share together
another Christmas." He stopped — into the chapel there
seemed to come a flooding as of God's presence. When the
Abbot spoke again, it was in a whisper, but all heard him:
"And now I ask our faithful stewards to go once again to the
cellars and storerooms and make sure that they saw only a
great emptiness when last they went."

It was a strange waiting for all who gathered in the refectory. Around bare tables that had held no food for two days
— and before that so scanty a serving that those who gathered
had almost forgotten what it meant to sit down to a full
meal — they waited and said nothing, so that when the
stewards burst into the room laden with enough to show how
full they had found the storehouses, the noise seemed almost
deafening. All but the Abbot looked in wonder at the loads
the stewards carried: hams and sides of bacon, bags of oaten
flour, cheeses, flagons of milk. All helped themselves sparingly, knowing full well how busy the cooks would be
throughout the days. Strangely enough none asked what
miracle had taken place to explain how empty shelves could
seemingly fill themselves in the space of a few hours.

Never had the abbey known a finer Christmas feast. The lads among themselves whispered their contentment and their wonder. Only Father Cumgall remained silent after the blessing had been spoken. Those watching him saw him gather at the end some cheese and pieces of the fresh bread baked and stow them away inside, where hung his pouch. Afterward he left all to their own devices, and going to his cell waited once again for the small whiskered nose to be thrust out of the hole in the corner, to be followed by the tidy body of a field mouse with white tips to tail and paws who waited for the Father's greeting: "You are most welcome, Brother Mouse. Again I have my dole of bread and cheese to share with you."

There followed the well-remembered scampering of feet and the swift climbing up the ragged robe until once again Brother Mouse perched on the Abbot's bony knee; and once again one wrinkled hand cupped itself around the small, sleek body. "I would have an accounting made concerning what happened during the night while the snow was falling."

Brother Mouse gave a small squeal of delight. "My great regret, good Father, is that you were not there to see what happened — both under the snow and above it. But this let me tell you: one of my kin sat unnoticed in the feasting hall when the King of Ulster's son laughed mockingly at God and you. He came quickly, bearing the news, and before the day was over every field mouse, every living creature who had lived through the drought was told. We found the storehouses and cellars of the castle unguarded. We left behind us not so much as a slice of cheese. This Christmas they do not believe in will be a hungry one. How all was carried I cannot explain, but the ways of God and small creatures are beyond telling. It is enough that there is enough to feed the abbey folk till the rains come and the planting is done, the grain reaped, and famine forgotten."

The eyes of the good Abbot had not twinkled since the swan had brought the sad warning of drought, nor had his eyes carried delight and fun in them. "As you say, Brother Mouse, the ways of God and small creatures are beyond telling. But carry our blessing — threefold — to the many thousands of your kin who must have brought this miracle to pass." He stopped and gave that hearty laugh he had given so often as he had led the four other Brothers years ago on their journey the length of all Ireland.

"In years to come, Brother Mouse, this will be reported as a miracle; and like as not the credit will be given to me. What is more absurd, I may be made a saint in good time. And what can I do about it? The Holy Father in Rome would scorn to canonize a mouse. But between ourselves, we know when all God's creatures, large and small, work together for the good of all, miracles are bound to happen."

And true it is that no other saint, Irish or otherwise, has ever been canonized because of what thousands of field mice did on a certain Christmas Eve long ago.